GCSE OCR Computer Science
for exams in 2022 and beyond

Practice Set A
Paper 1
Computer Systems

Time allowed:
- 1 hour 30 minutes

You **may not** use a calculator

| Centre name |
| Centre number |
| Candidate number |

| Surname |
| Other names |
| Candidate signature |

Instructions to candidates
- Write your name and other details in the spaces provided above.
- Answer **all** questions in the spaces provided.
- Do all rough work in this book. Cross through any work you do not want to be marked.

Information for candidates
- There are 80 marks available on this paper.
- The marks available are given in brackets at the end of each question.
- Quality of extended responses will be assessed in this paper in questions marked with an asterisk (*).

For examiner's use

Q	Attempt Nº	Q	Attempt Nº
1		6	
2		7	
3		8	
4		9	
5		Total	

Answer **all** questions in the spaces provided

1. Fergus owns a desktop computer with a 2.2 GHz quad-core CPU. He uses it to play video games and edit photographs that he takes with his digital camera.

(a) State the purpose of the CPU in a computer system.

....

....
[1 mark]

(b) Fergus' CPU uses Von Neumann architecture and features various registers. One of these registers is the MAR (Memory Address Register). State **one** other register used in Von Neumann architecture and the purpose of the register.

Register ....

Purpose ....

....
[2 marks]

(c) Fergus decides to purchase a new CPU with a higher clock speed compared to the one he currently owns. Explain, with reference to how Fergus uses his computer, the effect this will have on the computer's performance.

....

....

....
[2 marks]

(d) Fergus' computer has 8 GB of RAM. State the purpose of RAM in a computer.

....

....
[1 mark]

(e) Explain what is meant by 'virtual memory' and why it may be needed by a computer system.

....

....

....
[2 marks]

(f) Fergus' digital camera is an example of an 'embedded system'.

(i) Define the term 'embedded system'.

....

....
[1 mark]

(ii) Other than digital cameras, give **three** examples of embedded systems.

1 ....

2 ....

3 ....
[3 marks]

2. Freya is the network manager for CeraOTS, a large multi-national firm that publishes magazines in various languages. CeraOTS has offices in multiple countries, and these offices are connected to each other via a 'Wide Area Network' (WAN).

(a) Define the term 'Wide Area Network'.

....

....
[1 mark]

(b) Each CeraOTS office has its own LAN. Identify **one** piece of network hardware required to create a LAN and explain why this piece of hardware is needed.

Hardware required ....

Explanation ....

....

....
[2 marks]

(c) CeraOTS uses a client-server network setup. Describe, with an example, the relationship between client and server on the CeraOTS network.

....

....

....

....
[2 marks]

Turn over ▶

(d) Each office has a printer with built-in Wi-Fi® and Bluetooth® connectivity. For each statement below, tick (✓) the more appropriate wireless technology.

Statement	Wi-Fi®	Bluetooth®
More likely to have a higher bandwidth.		
More likely to have a longer connection range.		

[2 marks]

3. Mr Whorton is a teacher in a secondary school. He is considering storing student exam results using a cloud storage system.

(a) Explain a potential ethical and legal issue of Mr Whorton using the cloud to store students' data.

....

....

....

....

....

....

[4 marks]

(b) The secondary school uses both open source and proprietary software on its computer systems. State **two** differences between open source and proprietary software.

1 ....

....

2 ....

....

[2 marks]

(c) Mr Whorton learns that the school has been the victim of a cyber-attack. State the name of the law which is designed to prosecute hackers who gain access to computer systems without consent.

....

[1 mark]

4. Margaret owns a laptop computer which she occasionally uses to work from home. The laptop computer uses secondary storage.

(a) Define the term 'secondary storage'.

....
....
[1 mark]

(b) Explain why Margaret's laptop computer needs secondary storage.

....
....
....
[2 marks]

(c) Margaret's laptop computer has a Solid State Drive (SSD). Describe **one** benefit of having a SSD, rather than a Hard Disk Drive (HDD), in her laptop computer.

....
....
....
[2 marks]

(d) Margaret wants to transfer some large files from her work computer to her home laptop. Suggest **one** storage technology Margaret could use to transfer these files and explain why this is a suitable technology to use.

Storage technology ....

....

Explanation ....

....

....
[3 marks]

Turn over ▶

5. Dinesh is a cyber-security expert who has been employed by a large bank, XiBank, to discover potential vulnerabilities in their computer systems. XiBank are particularly worried about 'social engineering' attacks.

(a) (i) Define the term 'social engineering'.

....

....
[1 mark]

(ii) Describe **two** examples of social engineering attacks that could be used against XiBank.

1 ....

....

....

2 ....

....

....
[4 marks]

(b) Dinesh is concerned that XiBank's system is vulnerable to a 'denial of service' attack.

(i) Give the definition of a 'denial of service' attack.

....

....
[1 mark]

(ii) Identify **one** possible effect on XiBank of a denial of service attack.

....

....
[1 mark]

(c) State **three** security measures that Dinesh could put in place to increase the general security of XiBank's network.

1 ....
....
2 ....
....
3 ....
....
[3 marks]

6. Francesca works as a software engineer for Grenoside Software and is currently helping to develop a new Operating System (OS).

(a) The new OS will include 'multi-tasking' functions. Describe what is meant by 'multi-tasking', with reference to both the user and the CPU.

....
....
....
....
[2 marks]

(b) State **two** other functions of the Operating System in a computer system.

1 ....
2 ....
[2 marks]

(c) Francesca intends to include 'utility software' as part of the OS. State what is meant by 'utility software', and give **two** examples of it.

Definition ....
....

Examples 1 ....
2 ....
[3 marks]

Turn over ▶

7. (a) Complete the following sentence:

1 GB is equal to .... MB.

[1 mark]

(b) Convert the binary number 10011100 into denary.

....
....

[1 mark]

(c) Convert the hexadecimal number A4 into denary.
You must show your working.

....
....

[2 marks]

(d) A computer stores data and instructions in binary form.
Explain why computer systems use binary.

....
....

[2 marks]

(e) Add together the following two binary numbers:

```
  1 0 0 1 1 1 0 0 +
  0 0 1 1 0 0 1 0
  ───────────────
```

[2 marks]

(f) Perform a 1 place left shift on the binary number 00100101.

....
....

[1 mark]

8. Arthur has a media server in his home that he connects to with various devices over a LAN. His network uses a star network topology with a 'home hub' that combines the functions of a router, switch and wireless access point.

(a) State what is meant by the term 'network topology'.

....

....
[1 mark]

(b) Arthur has a desktop computer and a 'smart' TV connected to the network via wired connections, and his smartphone and his speakers both connect wirelessly. Draw a labelled diagram of the topology of Arthur's network.

[3 marks]

(c) While checking some settings on the media server, Arthur sees that each device connected to the server has a MAC address. State the purpose of a MAC address.

....

....

....
[1 mark]

Turn over ▶

(d) Arthur's network is connected to the Internet via his 'home hub'.
Network protocols are used during Internet communications.

The table below lists operations carried out by different network protocols.
Match the correct protocol to the corresponding operation.

Operation		Protocol
Downloading a JPEG image file from a remote server.		POP (Post Office Protocol)
Downloading an email at work from another colleague.		SMTP (Simple Mail Transfer Protocol)
Sending a party invitation over personal email to a group of friends.		HTTP (Hyper Text Transfer Protocol)
Accessing a celebrity's social media web page.		FTP (File Transfer Protocol)

[4 marks]

(e) Data transfer on a network involves the use of 'layers'.
State what is meant by the term 'layer' in this context.

....

....

....

[1 mark]

(f) When creating the 'home hub', the manufacturers had to meet certain network standards. Explain what a network standard is and why they are important.

....

....

....

....

[2 marks]

9. * Artificial Intelligence (AI) is becoming part of many people's day-to-day lives.

Examples include:
- the increased use of computers giving medical advice.
- website help assistants that respond to typed or spoken questions, imitating a conversation with a real person.
- social media websites that scan profiles to provide targeted adverts and information.

Discuss the impact of the increasing use of Artificial Intelligence (AI) in society.

In your answer, you might consider:
- cultural implications
- technology
- ethical implications
- environmental issues

....

....

....

....

....

....

....

....

....

....

....

....

....

....

....

....

....

Turn over ▶

[8 marks]

END OF QUESTIONS

GCSE OCR Computer Science
for exams in 2022 and beyond

Practice Set A
Paper 2
Computational Thinking, Algorithms and Programming

Centre name				
Centre number				
Candidate number				

Time allowed:
- 1 hour 30 minutes

Surname	
Other names	
Candidate signature	

You **may not** use a calculator

Instructions to candidates
- Write your name and other details in the spaces provided above.
- Answer **all** questions in the spaces provided.
- Do all rough work in this book. Cross through any work you do not want to be marked.

Information for candidates
- There are 80 marks available on this paper.
- The marks available are given in brackets at the end of each question.

For examiner's use

Q	Attempt Nº		Q	Attempt Nº	
1			5		
2			6		
3			7		
4					
			Total		

Answer **all** questions in the spaces provided

Section A

1. Khalid has written the following procedure, `printDetails`:

```
procedure printDetails (firstname, surname, age)
    print("My name is " + firstname + " " + surname
        + " and I am " + str(age) + " years old.")
    if age >= 17 then
        print("I am old enough to drive a car.")
    else
        print("I am not old enough to drive a car.")
    endif
endprocedure
```

(a) How many parameters does the procedure `printDetails` have?

....
[1 mark]

(b) What will be printed by the following call to the `printDetails` procedure?

`printDetails("Steve", "Wozniak", 66)`

....

....

....
[1 mark]

(c) Khalid learns that he can use both functions and procedures in a program. State the difference between a function and a procedure.

....

....

....
[1 mark]

2. Frankie is the manager of a day spa. He collects data about customers when they first book a session at the spa, which he stores in records.
A sample of this data is given in the table, `Customers`, shown below:

UserID	firstName	lastName	Gender	Paid
001	Shaun	Whorton	M	Yes
002	Sam	King	M	No
003	Tanya	Khayer	F	Yes

(a) Define the term 'record'.

....
[1 mark]

(b) Explain why Frankie might want to store the data in this structure.

....

....

....
[2 marks]

(c) Identify an appropriate data type that could be used to store whether or not the person had paid.

....
[1 mark]

(d) Frankie wants to know the full names of all customers who haven't paid for their sessions yet. Complete the SQL statement below to return this information.

SELECT ....

FROM Customers

WHERE Paid ....
[2 marks]

3. Gloria is planning to create a mobile application using a high-level programming language.

   (a) Explain **two** reasons why Gloria might prefer to program her mobile application using a high-level programming language rather than a low-level one.

   1 ....
   ....
   ....
   2 ....
   ....
   ....
   [4 marks]

   (b) Tick (✓) one box in each row of the table to show whether the statement refers to a feature of a compiler or an interpreter.

Feature	Compiler	Interpreter
Translates the whole program to produce an executable file		
Needed every time you want to run the program		
Halts the translation at the first line of error		

   [3 marks]

   (c) Gloria decides to use an Integrated Development Environment (IDE) to write her application. Identify **two** features of an IDE that she might use, and explain how they will assist in the development of the program.

   1 ....
   ....
   ....
   2 ....
   ....
   ....
   [4 marks]

4. Kulraj has designed a program using a flowchart, as shown:

Figure 1

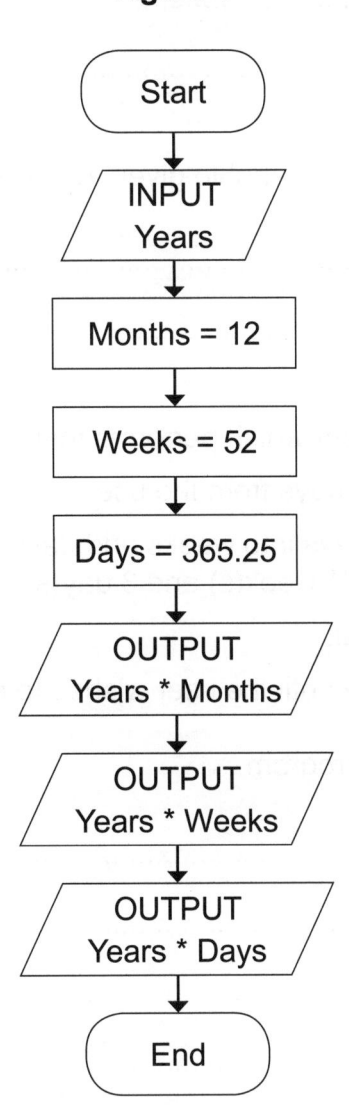

Start
↓
INPUT Years
↓
Months = 12
↓
Weeks = 52
↓
Days = 365.25
↓
OUTPUT Years * Months
↓
OUTPUT Years * Weeks
↓
OUTPUT Years * Days
↓
End

(a) Describe what the program has been designed to do.

....

....

....

[1 mark]

(b) Tick (✓) the programming construct that has been used in the flowchart.

Sequence ☐   Selection ☐   Iteration ☐

[1 mark]

Turn over ▶

(c) Identify **one** variable and **one** constant in the program.

Variable ....

Constant ....

[2 marks]

(d) Explain why you identified the variable given in part **(c)** as a variable.

....

....

[1 mark]

(e) Kulraj wants another program which performs these tasks:
- Input a whole number of days from the user.
- Convert the number of days into weeks and days, e.g. 10 days would give "1 week(s) and 3 day(s)".
- Print the result to the user.
- Repeat the bullets above until the user wishes to exit.

Write an algorithm for this program.

....

....

....

....

....

....

....

....

....

....

[5 marks]

5. Jordan is writing code for a travel website, and needs to choose suitable searching and sorting algorithms to use. He uses the following as test data:

Jakarta   London   Cairo   Minsk   Amsterdam   Bangkok

(a) Show the stages of a linear search to find the word "Amsterdam".

[4 marks]

(b) Show the stages of an insertion sort to put this list in alphabetical order.

[4 marks]

(c) Jordan's code will use the numbers 0-6 to represent the seven continents. He has created the following array:

```
array conts = ["Africa", "Antarctica", "Asia", "Australia",
               "Europe", "North America", "South America"]
```

Write an algorithm that:

- Asks for a user to input a number between 0 and 6.
- Checks the input is the correct data type and within the correct range.
- Outputs a message with the corresponding continent from the array or a description of the error if the input is not valid.

[6 marks]

6. (a) Draw a labelled logic circuit diagram for the following Boolean statement:

P = (A AND B) OR C

[3 marks]

(b) Complete the truth table for the logic statement P = (A AND B) OR C.
The first and last rows have been done for you.

A	B	C	P
FALSE	FALSE	FALSE	FALSE
TRUE	TRUE	TRUE	TRUE

[3 marks]

END OF SECTION A

Turn over ▶

Section B

Any questions that require you to give your answer in OCR Exam Reference Language or a high-level programming language will have specific instructions given in the question.

7. Grace is designing a program to run an online multiple choice quiz game. She has stored twenty questions in the file "r1_Q.txt" and has written the following pseudocode so far:

```
01    quizfile = open("r1_Q.txt")
02    quizScore = 0
03    for n = 1 to 20
04        nextQuestion = quizfile.readLine()
05        split nextQuestion into the variables
              question, answer1, answer2, answer3, correctAnsNum
06        print(question, answer1, answer2, answer3)
07        userAnswer = input("Enter 1, 2 or 3:")
```

(a) Tick (✓) the type of loop that has been used in the pseudocode.

Condition-Controlled ☐   Count-Controlled ☐

[1 mark]

(b) Explain the purpose of lines 04-05 in the pseudocode above.

....

....

....

....

....

....

[3 marks]

(c) Complete Grace's pseudocode, adding in the following functionality:

- Check whether the answer is correct and give an appropriate response to the user.
- Add 1 to the quiz score if they give a correct answer.
- At the end of the quiz, display the total score and close the file.

```
01   quizfile = open("r1_Q.txt")
02   quizScore = 0
03   for n = 1 to 20
04       nextQuestion = quizfile.readLine()
05       split nextQuestion into the variables
             question, answer1, answer2, answer3, correctAnsNum
06       print(question, answer1, answer2, answer3)
07       userAnswer = input("Enter 1, 2, or 3:")

08       if ………………………………………………………… then

09           print("Correct!")

10           quizScore = …………………………………………………

11       else

12           …………………………………………………

13       endif

14   next n

15   print("Your score is ", …………………………………, " out of 20")

16   …………………………………………………
```
[5 marks]

(d) Grace expands her program so that the quiz now consists of multiple rounds, each scored out of 20. She uses the two-dimensional array 'Scores', shown below, to store the results for 6 different players over 10 rounds (e.g. the third player's score in the eighth round is stored as Scores[2, 7]).

Round

	0	1	2	3	4	5	6	7	8	9
0	7	10	3	19	7	17	4	6	12	17
1	8	1	20	20	18	8	14	1	15	9
2	17	7	1	20	15	3	13	20	0	17
3	17	0	15	15	20	15	9	7	12	8
4	19	19	0	12	19	2	9	9	6	0
5	11	5	15	9	9	12	13	15	2	18

(Player on vertical axis)

Grace wants to know if any of the rounds are too easy or too difficult.
Write an algorithm to output the average (mean) score for each round.

[6 marks]

(e) Grace is designing a dice mini game to add to the end of each quiz round.

She has created a function, diceEven, which takes the value of two integers from 1 to 6. It adds the two integers together and returns either 'Even' or 'Odd', depending on if the sum is even or odd. For example, diceEven(2, 6) would return 'Even'.

Complete the program code for the function diceEven.

You must use either:
- OCR Exam Reference Language, or
- a high-level programming language that you have studied.

```
function ........................(x, y)

    total = ..........................................

    if ............................................ then

        outcome = "Even"

    else

        outcome = ..........................

    endif

    ..........................................

endfunction
```
[5 marks]

(f) Grace refines her quiz program to check whether a user is old enough to play the quiz. The program asks the user to enter their age and will only accept values of 18 or more as valid inputs.

Complete the following test plan for her program.

Test Data	Test Type	Accepted?
23		Yes
	Boundary	Yes
15		No
	Erroneous	No

[4 marks]

Turn over ▶

(g) Each player needs to have a username when playing the quiz.
Write a procedure that will:

- Ask a user to input their name and age.
- Return an error message if the user is younger than 18.
- Create a default username by concatenating the first three letters of their name (in uppercase) with their age if the user is 18 or older.

You must use either:
- OCR Exam Reference Language, or
- a high-level programming language that you have studied.

[6 marks]

END OF QUESTIONS

GCSE OCR Computer Science
for exams in 2022 and beyond

Practice Set B
Paper 1
Computer Systems

Centre name			
Centre number			
Candidate number			

Time allowed:
- 1 hour 30 minutes

Surname	
Other names	
Candidate signature	

You **may not** use a calculator

Instructions to candidates
- Write your name and other details in the spaces provided above.
- Answer **all** questions in the spaces provided.
- Do all rough work in this book. Cross through any work you do not want to be marked.

Information for candidates
- There are 80 marks available on this paper.
- The marks available are given in brackets at the end of each question.
- Quality of extended responses will be assessed in this paper in questions marked with an asterisk (*).

For examiner's use

Q	Attempt Nº		Q	Attempt Nº	
1			5		
2			6		
3			7		
4			8		
			Total		

Answer **all** questions in the spaces provided

1. Bryan is building a desktop computer system using various pieces of hardware.
   He purchases a dual-core CPU which features Von Neumann architecture.

   (a) State **one** characteristic of Von Neumann architecture.

   ....
   ....
   [1 mark]

   (b) Explain, with reference to memory and specific registers,
   the steps of the CPU fetch-execute cycle.

   ....
   ....
   ....
   ....
   ....
   ....
   ....
   [4 marks]

   (c) Bryan's computer system will have both RAM and ROM.
   Explain **two** differences between RAM and ROM.

   1 ....
   ....
   ....

   2 ....
   ....
   ....
   [4 marks]

(d) Describe how the Arithmetic Logic Unit (ALU) and the Accumulator work together in the CPU.

....

....

....
[2 marks]

(e) When Bryan finishes building his computer, he notices that it is quite slow, so he upgrades the CPU to one that is quad-core. Explain why doubling the number of cores will not necessarily double the performance of his system.

....

....

....

....

....

....

....
[3 marks]

Turn over ▶

2. Gail manages the storage of data across different departments at a large university. She is considering replacing the Hard Disk Drives (HDDs) on a number of servers with a different type of storage device.

   (a) State **two** characteristics of storage devices that Gail should take into consideration before upgrading the server storage.

   1 ....

   2 ....
   [2 marks]

   (b) Gail is considering cloud storage and magnetic tape as possible replacements. Compare the benefits and drawbacks of these two options for the university.

   ....

   ....

   ....

   ....

   ....

   ....

   ....

   ....

   ....
   [6 marks]

   (c) A professor needs some experimental data from one of the university servers. He asks Gail to make 30 copies of the data, each on a separate storage device so that they can be handed out to his students. The data is 5 GB in size.

   Briefly explain whether each of the following storage devices would be suitable to store the data on.

   CD-R optical discs ....

   ....

   USB pen drives ....

   ....

   External HDD ....

   ....
   [3 marks]

3. Paula is the manager of Penfold & Penfold, a talent agency which uses a wireless LAN in their office.

   (a) The computer systems at Penfold & Penfold feature various network-related hardware. One of these pieces of hardware is a Network Interface Controller (NIC). State why this piece of hardware is required.

   ....

   ....
   [1 mark]

   (b) Tick (✓) the piece of hardware below that would be required to connect Penfold & Penfold to an external network.

Switch	Router	Wireless Access Point

   [1 mark]

   (c) Paula is considering changing the wireless network to a wired network. Explain **one** advantage and **one** disadvantage of changing to a wired network.

   Advantage ....

   ....

   ....

   Disadvantage ....

   ....

   ....
   [4 marks]

   (d) The network setup at Penfold & Penfold is currently peer-to-peer. Describe **two** possible advantages of changing to a client-server network.

   1 ....

   ....

   ....

   2 ....

   ....

   ....
   [4 marks]

Turn over ▶

(e) While testing the network, Paula receives an error that says a device cannot connect to a DNS server. Describe the purpose of DNS servers in Internet communications.

....

....

....

[2 marks]

4. (a) Rank the following amounts of data in order of size, with 1 being the largest and 5 the smallest.

Data	Order of size
3 MB	
6 nibbles	
1.6 PB	
500 TB	
2 bytes	

[3 marks]

(b) '65' represents different numbers in the denary and hexadecimal systems.

(i) Convert 65 from a denary number into an 8-bit binary number.

....

....

[1 mark]

(ii) Convert 65 from a hexadecimal number into an 8-bit binary number.
You must show your working.

....

....

....

[2 marks]

(c) Add together the following two binary numbers:

```
1 0 0 1 1 1 1 1 +
0 0 1 1 1 1 0 1
```

[2 marks]

(d) An overflow error can occur when adding two 8-bit binary numbers. Describe what is meant by the term 'overflow error'.

....

....

[1 mark]

(e) Character sets are collections of characters that a computer recognises from their binary representation. One example of a character set is ASCII. State the name of another character set used in computer systems, and outline a feature of this character set.

Character set ....

Feature ....

....

[2 marks]

5. Nick regularly receives suspicious-looking emails claiming to be from banks, charities and other organisations. These emails often contain attachments.

    (a) State the name given to the practice of sending spoof emails.

    ....
    [1 mark]

    (b) Explain how anti-malware software can help to prevent malicious emails from attacking Nick's computer system.

    ....

    ....

    ....
    [2 marks]

    (c) The table below shows three pieces of malware that were identified on Nick's computer system by his anti-malware software. Tick **one** (✓) box in each row to show the type of malware that was identified in each case.

A piece of malware was...	Virus	Worm	Trojan
...found in an email attachment sent by an unfamiliar charity.			
...disguised as a popular open-source application.			
...self-replicating without interaction from Nick.			

    [3 marks]

6. Keil is a musician in a rock band. He regularly takes photographs of their concerts and posts them to social media sites.

(a) Explain why Keil might choose to not use the maximum image resolution when taking photographs with his camera.

....

....
[2 marks]

(b) State **two** pieces of metadata that could be included with a photograph.

1 ....

2 ....
[2 marks]

(c) Keil uses software to record himself playing the drums.

He uses a microphone to capture the sound. Explain how Keil's computer is able to create an audio file from this.

....

....

....
[2 marks]

(d) Keil needs to convert his audio files into a compressed format before uploading them to a web server. He can choose between formats with lossy and lossless compression. Describe **two** differences between lossy and lossless compression.

1 ....

....

....

2 ....

....

....
[4 marks]

Leave blank

Turn over ▶

7. Joel uses his desktop computer to trade on various stock markets around the world for his clients. He also stores a lot of sensitive data on his computer.

(a) Joel wants to purchase a new Operating System for his computer.
State **two** security measures that an OS may provide.

1 ....

2 ....
[2 marks]

(b) Joel plugs a printer into the computer and is asked to install a 'driver'.
Explain why Joel will need this 'driver'.

....

....

....
[2 marks]

(c) After regular use over several years, Joel notices that his computer system takes a long time to open files from his desktop. He notices that the Hard Disk Drive (HDD) appears to be making sounds more frequently.

(i) State the utility program Joel could use to potentially solve this problem.

....
[1 mark]

(ii) Explain how the utility program from (i) would improve the performance of Joel's Hard Disk Drive (HDD).

....

....

....

....
[3 marks]

8. * It is estimated that, globally, over a third of all paid-for software in use by both individuals and companies is pirated.

Discuss the impact of the increased use of pirated software on society.

In your answer, you might consider:
- impact on software developers
- legal issues
- ethical issues
- cultural implications

....

[8 marks]

END OF QUESTIONS

GCSE OCR Computer Science
for exams in 2022 and beyond

Practice Set B
Paper 2
Computational Thinking, Algorithms and Programming

Centre name				
Centre number				
Candidate number				

Time allowed:
- 1 hour 30 minutes

Surname	
Other names	
Candidate signature	

You **may not** use a calculator

Instructions to candidates
- Write your name and other details in the spaces provided above.
- Answer **all** questions in the spaces provided.
- Do all rough work in this book. Cross through any work you do not want to be marked.

Information for candidates
- There are 80 marks available on this paper.
- The marks available are given in brackets at the end of each question.

For examiner's use

Q	Attempt Nº		Q	Attempt Nº	
1			5		
2			6		
3			7		
4					
			Total		

Exam Set COP42

Answer **all** questions in the spaces provided

Section A

1. (a) Draw lines to match each logic diagram to the correct Boolean logic statement.

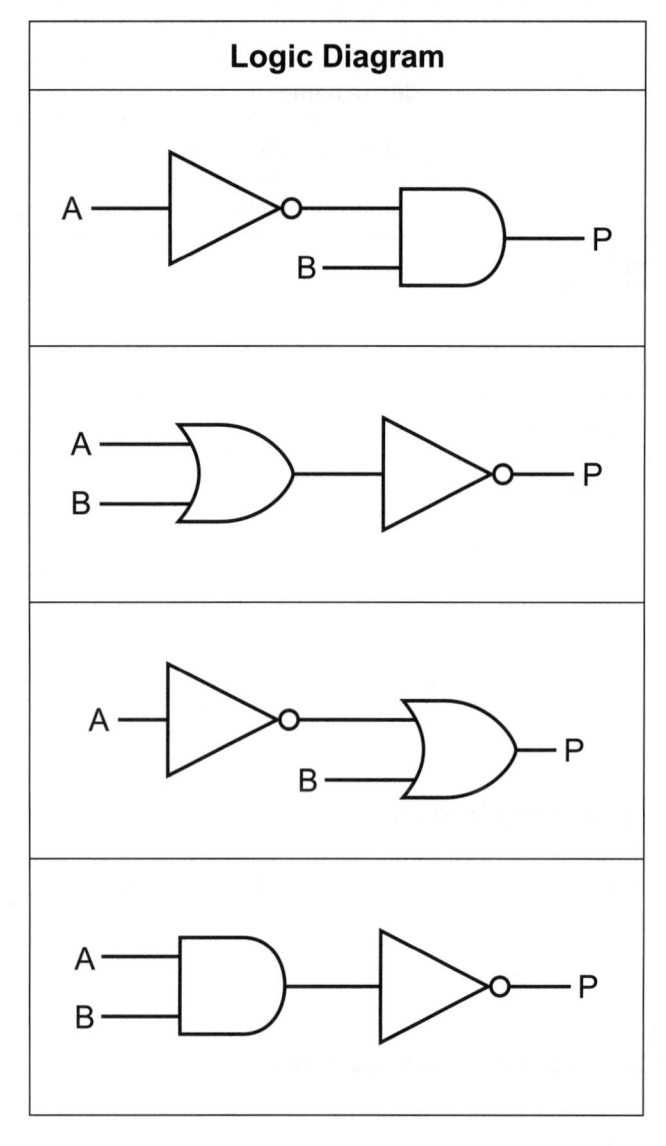

Logic Diagram	Boolean Logic
(NOT A) AND B gate diagram	P = (NOT A) OR B
(A OR B) then NOT diagram	P = (NOT A) AND B
(NOT A) OR B diagram	P = NOT (A AND B)
(A AND B) then NOT diagram	P = NOT (A OR B)

[2 marks]

(b) Complete the truth table for the logic statement P = (NOT A) AND B.

A	B	P

[2 marks]

(c) The main entrance to a university library uses Boolean logic to determine whether or not the door will open. The door requires a person to scan their library card. It then prompts them to enter a 4-digit passcode.

The door will only open if the library card is valid, the passcode is correct, and the time of day is between 7:00 and 18:00.

Write an algorithm for this program that includes the use of Boolean variables named `librarycardValid`, `passcodeValid` and `openDoor`.

[5 marks]

2. A travel company uses a database table `holiday` to store their current holiday destinations with their duration (in weeks) and cost (in pounds). An excerpt of the table is shown below.

Destination	Duration	Cost
Amsterdam	1	90
Muscat	2	250
Reykjavik	2	150
Buenos Aires	1	1000

A customer has a budget of £400 to spend on a holiday.
Write an SQL statement to return all destinations the customer can afford to visit.

[3 marks]

3. A server uses a program to ensure that all files saved to it have valid filenames.

When a user saves a file to the server, a prompt asks them to enter a filename. If the filename is over 30 characters long, then it will respond with a prompt stating the type of error and asking the user to rename the file. Once a valid name is chosen, the file is saved to the server and a confirmation message, which includes the final filename, is displayed to the user.

(a) Complete the pseudocode for this program.

```
filenameValid = false

do

    filename = ................................................................

    if ................................................................ > 30 then

        print("Filename too long.")

    else

        filenameValid = true

    endif

until ................................................................................

save file to server as filename

print ................................................................................
```
[4 marks]

(b) Give **one** other validation check that would be appropriate for this program.

....
[1 mark]

(c) Using input validation in a program is an example of 'defensive design'.

(i) Outline what is meant by 'defensive design'.

....

....
[1 mark]

(ii) Give **one** problem of a program having lots of input validation.

....

....
[1 mark]

4. Vivienne has a list of fruit and vegetables stored in a data structure.

| Grape | Pear | Tomato | Fig | Mango | Kale | Apple | Cherry |

(a) Tick (✓) the most appropriate data structure to store the data above.

Record	**Array**	**String**

[1 mark]

(b) Use a merge sort algorithm to arrange this data in alphabetical order, showing each stage of the process clearly.

....

....

....

....

....

....

....

[4 marks]

(c) Show the stages of a binary search, used on the sorted list, to find 'Cherry'.

....

....

....

....

....

....

....

[4 marks]

(d) Give **one** other searching algorithm that Vivienne could use.

....

[1 mark]

Turn over ▶

5. Julian is writing some software to help him process and store temperature data.
To assist with programming, he is using an Integrated Development Environment (IDE).

(a) The IDE that Julian is using offers many common tools and facilities.
Outline how the following features will help Julian develop his program:

Error diagnostics ....

....

....

Run-time environment ....

....

....

[2 marks]

(b) Julian uses both 'iterative testing' and 'final testing' for his program.
Describe the difference between these types of testing.

....

....

....

....

[2 marks]

(c) To convert temperatures from Fahrenheit to Celsius,
subtract 32 from the temperature in Fahrenheit, then divide by 1.8.
Julian's code includes a subprogram, `convertFC`, which is designed to do this.
His first draft of the code is given below:

```
function convertFC(temp)
    C == temp - 32 / 1.8
    return C
endfunction
```

Identify a logic error and a syntax error in Julian's code.

Logic error ....

....

Syntax error ....

....

[2 marks]

(d) Julian needs to write a program with the following functionality:
- Open a text file called 'Daily_Temps.txt'.
- Allow the user to input a temperature (in Fahrenheit) as many times as they want.
- Write all temperatures in Celsius to 'Daily_Temps.txt'.
- Close the file once finished.

Write an algorithm for this program. You should use the `convertFC` function and assume that any errors in it have been corrected.

....
....
....
....
....
....
....
....
....

[6 marks]

6. Tabitha is designing a control system for her greenhouse.
She plans the program by drawing a structure diagram, as shown below.

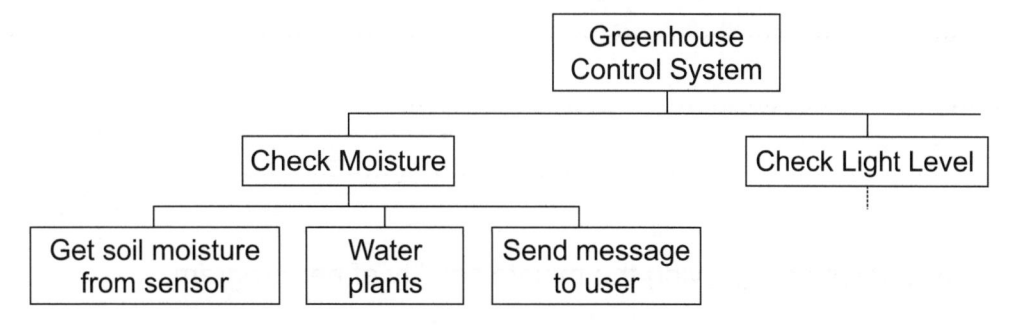

```
                    Greenhouse
                  Control System
                  /             \
          Check Moisture      Check Light Level
         /      |      \
Get soil    Water     Send message
moisture    plants    to user
from sensor
```

(a) Give **two** benefits of using structure diagrams to plan a program.

1 ....
....

2 ....
....

[2 marks]

Turn over ▶

The following program code is part of the 'Check Moisture' module.

```
01    if soilMoisture < 30 then
02      do
03        water = true
04        wait(3)  // waits for the given number of seconds
05        soilMoisture = soilMoisture + 1.5
06      until soilMoisture > 50
07      print("Watering complete")
08      water = false
09    else
10      print("No watering needed")
11    endif
```

(b) State the line (or lines) in Tabitha's code where the following features appear.

Feature	Line(s)
Boolean data	
Iteration	
String data	

[3 marks]

(c) Tabitha's code assumes that 3 seconds of watering will increase the soil moisture level by 1.5. Tabitha decides that this figure is inaccurate and changes line 05 to the following.

```
05    soilMoisture = soilMoisture + 1.2
```

Explain how this change will affect the amount of water the plants receive.

....

....

....

[2 marks]

(d) Outline **two** ways of improving the maintainability of her program.

1 ....

....

2 ....

....

[2 marks]

END OF SECTION A

Section B

Any questions that require you to give your answer in OCR Exam Reference Language or a high-level programming language will have specific instructions given in the question.

7. Claudio is the manager of a bookshop. He uses various programs to help run his store. The program below is used to generate a book code for a given book.

   ```
   title = input("Enter title of book")
   x = title.length
   y = "2020"
   if x < 7 then
       print("Invalid input")
   else
       for i = 0 to 6 step 2
           y = y + title.subString(i, 1)
       next i
       print(y)
   endif
   ```

   (a) (i) Explain why variable y should be stored as a string.

   ....

   ....
   [2 marks]

   (ii) Complete the trace table for the program if a user enters "Ferret!"

x	i	y
7	—	"2020"

   [4 marks]

(b) Claudio wants to test his program. Some test data is shown below. Tick (✓) **one** box in each row to show what type each piece of data is.

	Normal	Invalid	Boundary	Erroneous
"Moon Centaurs"				
"Outpost"				
"Luna"				

[3 marks]

Turn over ▶

Claudio would like to design a program to be used by customers in store.
The program should choose a random book genre from a 1D array `genres`
and print the suggestion to the customer.

(c) Complete the code below for this program.

You must use either:
- OCR Exam Reference Language, or
- a high-level programming language that you have studied.

```
array genres = ["Fantasy", "Crime", "Romance",
                "Sci-Fi", "Western"]
```

....

....

....

....

[3 marks]

The bookshop also sells a selection of audiobooks.

Claudio writes the function `fileSize()` which takes a filename as a parameter and returns the size (in GB) of the file.

He wants to use his function in a program which takes a filename of an audiobook as a user input and checks whether the file size is less than 1.5 GB.
If it isn't, an alert message is displayed to the user.

(d) Complete the code below for this program.

You must use either:
- OCR Exam Reference Language, or
- a high-level programming language that you have studied.

```
fileName = ......................................................................................

audioSize = fileSize(..................................................)

if ............................................................ then

    print ......................................................................................

endif
```

[4 marks]

Claudio is designing a program to calculate each staff member's sales over the month. The program then calculates a pay bonus. He has written the following program code.

```
01   do
02       name = input("Enter staff name")
03       total = 0
04       do
05           sales = input("Enter value of item sold (£)")
06           total = total + sales
07       until sales == 0
08       bonus = total * 0.1
09       print(name + " gets a £" + str(bonus) + " bonus.")
10       continue = input("Continue? (Y/N)")
11   until continue == "N"
```

(e) Identify which programming construct has been used.
Tick (✓) the correct box in the table.

Sequence	Selection	Iteration

[1 mark]

(f) State the purpose of the following lines in the algorithm above.

03 ....

06 ....

07 ....

08 ....

[4 marks]

(g) Give the output of the program if Claudio inputs the following data:

Jesse, 60, 120, 20, 0, Y, Anabelle, 70, 50, 40, 0, Y, Roland, 19, 11, 0, N

....

....

....

[3 marks]

Turn over ▶

(h) Claudio wants to refine his code, with the following functionality added:
- Increase the bonus to 15% if the employee has sold more than £500 of books.
- Decrease the bonus to 5% if the employee has sold £100 of books or less.
- Display an error message if a sales input is a negative number.

Write the refined version of the program.

You must use either:
- OCR Exam Reference Language, or
- a high-level programming language that you have studied.

[6 marks]

END OF QUESTIONS

CGP

GCSE OCR
Computer Science

For the Grade 9-1 Course

Practice Exam Papers
Instructions & Answer Book

Optimise your GCSE Computer Science exam prep with CGP...

Let's face it, OCR's Grade 9-1 Computer Science exams are tougher than a 1980s arcade game. Fortunately, our practice papers are just what you'll need to become a highly efficient exam-passing machine.

We've included two full sets of papers, designed to look, feel, and maybe even smell just like what you'll get in the exam. You'll also find detailed answers and mark schemes in this booklet. Very handy.

So dust off those programming skills — soon you'll be writing algorithms in your sleep.

Published by CGP

Contributors: Shaun Whorton.

Editors: Liam Dyer, Sammy El-Bahrawy, and Michael Weynberg.

Proofreaders: Neil Hastings and Simon Little.

With thanks to Lottie Edwards for the copyright research.

Clipart from Corel®
Printed by Elanders Ltd, Newcastle upon Tyne.

Text, design, layout and original illustrations
© Coordination Group Publications Ltd. (CGP) 2020
All rights reserved.

Photocopying more than 5% of a paper is not permitted, even if you have a CLA licence.
Extra copies are available from CGP with next day delivery • 0800 1712 712 • www.cgpbooks.co.uk

What to Expect in The Exams

Topics are Covered in Different Papers

For OCR GCSE Computer Science, you'll sit **two exam papers** at the **end** of your course.

Paper	Topics include...	Time	Number of marks
1	Computer systems, networks, software and real-world issues.	1 hr 30 mins	80
2	Computational thinking, algorithms and programming skills.	1 hr 30 mins	80

Paper 2 has two sections — **Section A** is worth **50 marks** and **Section B** is worth **30 marks**.

The exams will include some Extended Writing...

Paper 1 will include one **extended response** question, where you'll have to write at length on a particular **topic** and consider its impact in different areas. Your answer will need to be well-written, clearly-structured and make **loads of good points**, not just waffle to fill the space. The only way to get these questions right is by carefully **planning** out your answer first.

Questions like this will be marked with a *.

...and a healthy dose of Programming Skills

- Many questions in Paper 2 will present you with algorithms written in **pseudocode**, **OCR Exam Reference Language** or as a **flowchart**. There's more info on OCR Exam Reference Language at the back of the **OCR specification**.

- You may be asked to **write your own algorithms or code** — if the question doesn't give you any specific instructions, you have **flexibility** on how you present your answer. You can use **pseudocode**, **OCR Exam Reference Language**, a **high-level programming language** or a **flowchart**. Stick with whichever you find easier.

- In Section B, there are **specific instructions** for some questions. You **must** use a **programming language** in your answer to get **any marks** — either **OCR Exam Reference Language** or a **high-level programming language** you have studied.

All the algorithm answers in this booklet are just examples — there are loads of ways that you could answer each question.

Marking Your Papers

- Do a complete exam (Paper 1 and Paper 2).
- Use the answers and mark scheme in this booklet to mark each exam paper.
- Write down your mark for each paper in the table below — each paper is worth a maximum of 80 marks.
- Find your total for the whole exam (out of a maximum of 160 marks) by adding up your marks from both papers.
- Follow the instructions below to estimate your grade.

	Paper 1	Paper 2	Total	Grade
SET A				
SET B				

Estimating Your Grade

- If you want to get a **rough idea** of the grade you're working at, we suggest you compare the **total mark** you got in **each set** to the latest set of grade boundaries.
- Grade boundaries are set for each individual exam, so they're likely to **change** from year to year. You can find the latest set of grade boundaries by going to **www.cgpbooks.co.uk/gcsegradeboundaries**
- Jot down the marks required for each grade in the table below so you don't have to refer back to the website. Use these marks to **estimate your grade**. If you're borderline, don't push yourself up a grade — the real examiners won't.

Total mark required for each grade									
Grade	9	8	7	6	5	4	3	2	1
Total mark out of 160									

- Remember, this will only be a **rough guide**, and grade boundaries will be different for different exams, but it should help you to see how you're getting on.

Answers

Set A — Paper 1

1. a) E.g.
   - The CPU processes data and instructions. *[1 mark]*
   - The CPU fetches, decodes and executes program instructions. *[1 mark]*

   [1 mark available in total]

   b) Any **one** register with its purpose, e.g.
   - Memory Data Register (MDR) *[1 mark]* — holds data or instructions waiting to be processed or moved to RAM. *[1 mark]*
   - Program Counter (PC) *[1 mark]* — points to the next instruction to be executed. *[1 mark]*
   - Accumulator *[1 mark]* — stores the results of calculations carried out by the Arithmetic Logic Unit (ALU). *[1 mark]*

   [2 marks available in total]

   c) E.g.
   The computer will be able to execute more instructions per second. *[1 mark]* So his video games may appear to run more smoothly/have a higher frame rate *[1 mark]* and his photo editing software may run faster. *[1 mark]*

   [2 marks available in total]

   d) RAM stores data/instructions/software/files while they are in use by the system. *[1 mark]*

   e) Virtual memory is the allocation of an area of secondary storage to be used like RAM. *[1 mark]* It is needed to allow the computer to open additional files/applications when RAM is full. *[1 mark]*

   f) i) Embedded systems are computers that are built into a larger system. *[1 mark]*

   ii) Any **three** examples, e.g.
   - dishwashers *[1 mark]*
   - televisions *[1 mark]*
   - washing machines *[1 mark]*
   - sat navs *[1 mark]*

   [3 marks available in total]

2. a) A Wide Area Network connects computers/LANs that are in different geographical locations. *[1 mark]*

   b) Any **one** piece of hardware with a suitable explanation, e.g.
   - Switch/Wireless Access Point (WAP) *[1 mark]* — directs data on the network. *[1 mark]*
   - Network Interface Card (NIC) *[1 mark]* — allows individual devices to connect to the network. *[1 mark]*
   - Ethernet cable *[1 mark]* — carries the data between devices on the network. *[1 mark]*

   [2 marks available in total]

   c) Client-server relationship:
   The client computer systems send requests to the server for data/services. The server processes and responds to requests from multiple clients. *[1 mark]*
   OR
   The server centrally stores data, e.g. documents, emails, passwords, etc. and manages how clients can access this data. *[1 mark]*
   Examples:
   - requesting a magazine article from the file server. *[1 mark]*
   - using a client machine to send an email via the email server to a freelance writer. *[1 mark]*

   [2 marks available — 1 mark for explanation of client-server relationship, 1 mark for a suitable example]

   d)
Statement	Wi-Fi®	Bluetooth®
More likely to have a higher bandwidth.	✓	
More likely to have a longer connection range.		✓

   [2 marks available — 1 mark for each correct row]

3. a) E.g.
   Ethical issues:
   - Mr Whorton is placing the students' personal data in the hands of a third party, *[1 mark]* meaning he can't fully guarantee that it is safe, e.g. the cloud site might be hacked. *[1 mark]*
   - The data itself will be stored off-site, *[1 mark]* so unless the school keeps a local backup, the data could be lost if anything happens to the cloud storage company's servers. *[1 mark]*

   Legal issues:
   - The Data Protection Act states that sensitive documents must be kept safe and secure. *[1 mark]* If he stores the data on a cloud storage service, Mr Whorton will have little control over its security. *[1 mark]*
   - The Data Protection Act states that data must not be kept for longer than necessary. *[1 mark]* Mr Whorton will have no control over whether the cloud storage company back up or copy the data, so he won't be able to ensure that it has been completely deleted when it is no longer needed. *[1 mark]*

   [4 marks available in total — one ethical and one legal issue must both be covered for full marks]

   Ethical and legal issues are both about what's right and wrong, but ethical means in the eyes of society and legal means in the eyes of the law.

   b) Any **two** differences, e.g.
   - Open source software is usually free, while proprietary software is usually paid for. *[1 mark]*
   - Open source software can be legally modified by anyone, while the modification of proprietary software is restricted. *[1 mark]*
   - Open source software can often contain bugs and security flaws, while proprietary software tends to be well-tested and reliable, with frequent patches and updates. *[1 mark]*
   - Open source software is usually only supported by online communities, whereas proprietary software will usually come with warranties, documentation and customer support. *[1 mark]*

   [2 marks available in total]

   c) The Computer Misuse Act 1990. *[1 mark]*

4. a) Secondary storage is a computer's non-volatile internal storage. *[1 mark]*

   b) The laptop computer needs secondary storage to store data/programs/its operating system *[1 mark]* when it is not in use/when the power has been switched off. *[1 mark]*

   c) Any **one** reason, e.g.
   - SSDs have no moving parts, *[1 mark]* making them more robust / shockproof than HDDs, particularly in portable devices which are frequently moved when in use. *[1 mark]*
   - SSDs have fast read-write speeds, *[1 mark]* so programs and files will load faster than if they were on a HDD. *[1 mark]*

   [2 marks available in total]

d) Any **one** storage technology with a suitable explanation, e.g.
- Memory card/SD card *[1 mark]*
  - They tend to have a high storage capacity, so they are suitable for storing large files. *[1 mark]*
  - They are very small, making them convenient for Margaret to bring to and from work. *[1 mark]*
- Cloud storage *[1 mark]*
  - It would be convenient as Margaret would not need to physically transport anything. *[1 mark]*
  - Cloud storage doesn't require any additional hardware or specific ports. *[1 mark]*
  - Certain cloud storage services are free, and paid ones are usually cheap for the amount of storage they provide. *[1 mark]*
- USB pen drive *[1 mark]*
  - USB pen drives are often relatively cheap and easy to obtain. *[1 mark]*
  - Most USB pen drives are small and portable, making them convenient for transferring data between devices. *[1 mark]*
  - It will be compatible with both machines — desktop computers and laptops always have USB ports. *[1 mark]*

[3 marks available in total — 1 mark for a suitable storage technology and 2 marks for relevant explanations]

5. a) i) Social engineering is a way of gaining illegal access to sensitive information/private networks by influencing people. *[1 mark]*

   ii) Any **two** examples, e.g.
   - A phishing email is sent to the employees or customers of XiBank, *[1 mark]* pretending to be from an official source and tricking them into inputting their login details. *[1 mark]*
   - An employee or customer of XiBank receives a spoof phone call *[1 mark]* from someone pretending to be someone else within the company and asking them to disclose their login details. *[1 mark]*
   - A spoof version of the official XiBank website is created, *[1 mark]* where employees or customers can be tricked into entering their login details. *[1 mark]*

   [4 marks available in total]

b) i) A denial of service attack is where an attacker prevents access to a network or website by flooding it with useless traffic. *[1 mark]*

   ii) Any **one** effect, e.g.
   - Customers are unable to withdraw their money. *[1 mark]*
   - Customers are unable to access their online account/the website runs very slowly. *[1 mark]*
   - Employees are unable to use the network/it becomes extremely slow. *[1 mark]*

   [1 mark available in total]

c) Any **three** measures, e.g.
- Penetration testing *[1 mark]*
- Installing physical security such as locks and surveillance equipment. *[1 mark]*
- Requiring strong passwords from all users *[1 mark]*
- Setting up user access levels on the network *[1 mark]*
- Installing anti-malware software on all networked computers *[1 mark]*
- Encrypting all sensitive data on the network *[1 mark]*
- Educating employees in how to spot phishing scams *[1 mark]*

[3 marks available in total]

6. a) E.g. Multi-tasking allows more than one application to appear to the user to be running at the same time *[1 mark]* while in fact the Operating System is just efficiently managing memory and CPU processing time to simulate this. *[1 mark]*

   b) Any **two** functions, e.g.
   - Communicating with hardware *[1 mark]*
   - Providing a User Interface (UI) *[1 mark]*
   - File and disk management *[1 mark]*
   - Managing user accounts/security *[1 mark]*

   [2 marks available in total]

   c) Utility software is used to help to maintain or configure a computer. *[1 mark]*
   Any **two** examples, e.g.
   - disk defragmentation utilities *[1 mark]*
   - compression software *[1 mark]*
   - encryption software *[1 mark]*
   - disk restore utilities *[1 mark]*
   - anti-virus software *[1 mark]*
   - firewalls *[1 mark]*
   - automatic update utilities *[1 mark]*

   [3 marks available in total]

7. a) 1 GB is equal to 1000 MB
   [1 mark — allow 1024 as alternative answer]

   b) Convert each '1' bit into denary using its place value:
   10011100 = 128 + 16 + 8 + 4 = 156 *[1 mark]*

   c) A in hexadecimal = 10 in binary,
   so A0 = 10 × 16 = 160 *[1 mark]*
   and A4 = 160 + 4 = 164 *[1 mark]*

   d) Computers work using logic circuits, which use on/off or true/false states, *[1 mark]* so numbers need to be processed in a format that can represent on/off states, i.e. in binary as 1s and 0s. *[1 mark]*

   e)   1 0 0 1 1 1 0 0 +
        0 0 1 1 0 0 1 0
        ─────────────
        1 1 0 0 1 1 1 0
          1 1

   [2 marks available — 1 mark for each correct nibble]

   f) 01001010 *[1 mark]*
   Remember, a 1 place left shift just means moving each digit one spot to the left, and sticking a 0 on the end.

8. a) Network topology refers to the layout of the network/the arrangement of the devices in the network. *[1 mark]*

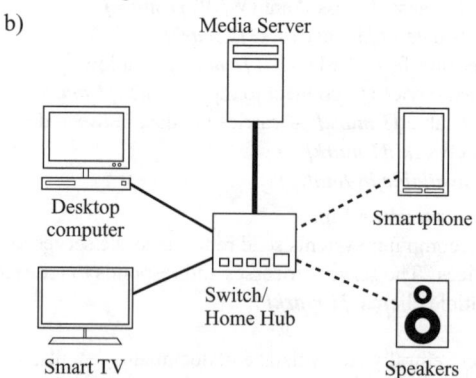

   b) [Diagram: Media Server connected to Switch/Home Hub, with Desktop computer wired to switch, and Smartphone, Smart TV, Speakers connected]

   [3 marks available — 1 mark for all devices connected to a central switch/hub, 1 mark for a distinction between wired and wireless device connections and 1 mark for the switch/hub connecting to the media server]
   No marks for artistic ability (sadly), so don't get carried away with beautiful illustrations of each device. A labelled box will do.

   c) A MAC address is a unique identifier for a device, which allows it to be found on a network. *[1 mark]*

d)

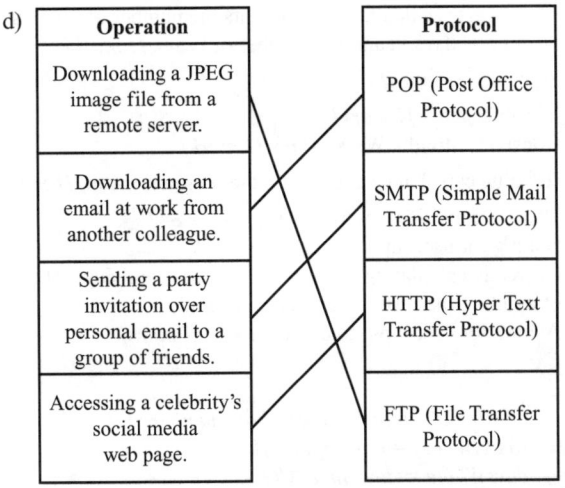

Operation	Protocol
Downloading a JPEG image file from a remote server.	POP (Post Office Protocol)
Downloading an email at work from another colleague.	SMTP (Simple Mail Transfer Protocol)
Sending a party invitation over personal email to a group of friends.	HTTP (Hyper Text Transfer Protocol)
Accessing a celebrity's social media web page.	FTP (File Transfer Protocol)

Connections:
- Downloading a JPEG image file from a remote server → FTP
- Downloading an email at work from another colleague → POP
- Sending a party invitation over personal email to a group of friends → SMTP
- Accessing a celebrity's social media web page → HTTP

[4 marks available — 1 mark for each correct connection]

e) A layer is a self-contained group of network protocols which have similar functions. *[1 mark]*

f) A network standard is a set of agreed requirements for hardware and software. *[1 mark]*
They are important as they ensure manufacturers create products and programs that will be compatible with products and programs from other manufacturers. *[1 mark]*

9. Points you might include:

Cultural implications
- People could become more isolated with the increased use of AI, rather than, for example, seeking face-to-face appointments with human medical professionals.
- Companies may be able to save costs by employing fewer customer service staff and using AIs in their place.
- AI assistants may not be able to provide the same quality of service as a human could — this could lead to a lower standard of customer service in general.
- AIs could provide services such as personalised news and scheduling assistance, making daily life more convenient.
- AI services could be adapted to include advertisements, further intruding on our day-to-day lives.
- AI-tailored adverts are, in theory, relevant to the user, which could increase a user's interest in the adverts and make them more useful to them.
- People may feel pressured into buying the latest AI technology to keep up with what may be considered 'basic needs', and they may struggle to afford this. This could further increase the digital divide.

Technology
- Widespread use of AI will encourage the development of improvements to the technology, e.g. 'smarter' AI, faster service, better personalised service, etc.
- Many AI technologies, such as speech recognition, work by collecting and analysing massive amounts of user data to become 'smarter', so as more people use AI services, more data will be collected and the 'smarter' it will become.
- The current technology is still very limited, which may discourage people from investing time and money into its development.
- The development of AI could lead to innovation in other areas of machine learning, such as weather systems, or to developments in hardware in fields like robotics.

Ethical implications
- The AI systems may ask you to provide personal information in order to use the service, which may be made available to other parties without the user knowing (e.g. if the user agrees to an End User Licence Agreement without reading it carefully).
- As AIs develop to perform advanced tasks such as giving medical advice, they may reduce the need for people in these jobs, which may cause unemployment.
- If services such as medical advice become quicker and easier to access, it may help injured people or even save lives.
- Some people may be uncomfortable with the idea of 'creating intelligence', seeing it as ethically or religiously wrong (e.g. 'playing God').
- The human-like conversation may intimidate users who do not feel comfortable 'talking' to an AI that acts human.
- People may see the data collection required by AIs as an invasion of privacy — users may have their speech recorded by an AI assistant, or their movements tracked by their smart GPS, without necessarily being aware of it.
- The technology could be adapted to be used for illegal purposes, such as hacking.
- AI could read people's social media profiles to determine their social background, political/religious views, etc. Targeted messages could then be sent to these people to subtly influence their views, e.g. in a political election campaign.

Environmental issues
- Advances in AI technology may require more and more cutting-edge hardware, meaning that more precious metals will be used up.
- As more 'smart' devices are released, people will dispose of their old devices, causing the world's landfill sites to fill quickly. In the long term, this could pose an environmental risk at these sites.
- People could seek medical advice from AIs at home rather than driving to see a human professional, which could reduce emissions from cars and other vehicles.

How to mark your answer:
- Two or three brief points with very little explanation. *[1-2 marks]*
- Three to five detailed points covering at least two of: cultural implications, technology, ethical implications and environmental issues. *[3-5 marks]*
- Six or more detailed points that form a well-written, balanced discussion, covering all of: cultural implications, technology, ethical implications and environmental issues. *[6-8 marks]*

I feel a sudden urge to clear my social calendar for a week, order lots of pizza and settle in to watch back-to-back Blade Runner 2049, The Matrix, Westworld, WarGames, 2001, Tron, Tron Legacy, Ex Machina, Terminator 1, Terminator 2, maybe even Terminator 3...
You'll have time to do the same after your GCSEs...

Set A — Paper 2

1. a) Three *[1 mark]*
   b) My name is Steve Wozniak and I am 66 years old.
      I am old enough to drive a car. *[1 mark]*
   c) Functions always return a value, while procedures don't. *[1 mark]*

2. a) A record is a type of data structure that stores data entries/fields. *[1 mark]*
   b) E.g. Records allow Frankie to store each customer's data in a fixed structure/collection of fields *[1 mark]* with different data types (arrays only allow a single data type) *[1 mark]*.
      This means that he can easily retrieve specific parts of the data, e.g. the User IDs of all the customers who have not paid. *[1 mark]*
      [2 marks available in total]
   c) Boolean *[1 mark]*
   d) SELECT firstName, lastName *[1 mark]*
      From Customers
      WHERE Paid = "No" *[1 mark]*

3. a) Any **two** reasons, e.g.
   - High-level programming languages use commands that more closely resemble normal text, *[1 mark]* so they would be quicker and easier to work with. *[1 mark]*
   - Fewer lines of code are required to carry out the same tasks with high-level languages, *[1 mark]* so it would take less time to write the necessary code. *[1 mark]*
   - High-level languages are easier to read and debug *[1 mark]* so it will be easier to fix any errors in the code at the development stage. *[1 mark]*
   - Code written in a low-level language tends to only work for one specific machine or processor, *[1 mark]* so a high-level language might make it easier for the application to work on different mobile devices. *[1 mark]*
   [4 marks available in total]

   b)
Feature	Compiler	Interpreter
Translates the whole program to produce an executable file	✓	
Needed every time you want to run the program		✓
Halts the translation at the first line of error		✓

   [3 marks available — 1 mark for each correct row]

   c) Any **two** features, e.g.
   - Auto-complete *[1 mark]* — will save time while writing code by completing the typing of variables and functions. *[1 mark]*
   - Debugger *[1 mark]* — will inform Gloria of the location of errors, and often suggest how to fix it. *[1 mark]*
   - Explorer window *[1 mark]* — will help her to navigate through long programs. *[1 mark]*
   - Breakpoints *[1 mark]* — will help Gloria to track errors in the middle of a program by pausing it at certain points. *[1 mark]*
   - Auto-colour coding *[1 mark]* — will help her to distinguish between variables, functions, comments, etc. *[1 mark]*
   [4 marks available in total]

4. a) The program calculates and outputs the number of months, weeks and days in a given number of years. *[1 mark]*
   b) Sequence *[1 mark]*
   c) Variable: Years *[1 mark]*
      Constant: Months/Weeks/Days *[1 mark]*
   d) Its value can change every time the program is run. *[1 mark]*
   e) Using a condition-controlled loop. *[1 mark]*
      Asking for user input for days. *[1 mark]*
      Correctly calculating the number of weeks and days. *[1 mark]*
      Outputting the result to the user. *[1 mark]*
      Asking for user input to exit the loop. *[1 mark]*
      E.g.
      do
         daysInput = input("Enter whole number of days.")
         weeksWhole = daysInput DIV 7
         daysWhole = daysInput MOD 7
         print(str(weeksWhole) + " week(s) and "
            str(daysWhole) + " days(s)")
         exit = input("Enter X to exit loop.")
      until exit = "X"

5. a) <u>Jakarta</u> London Cairo Minsk Amsterdam Bangkok
      Not Amsterdam, continue:
      Jakarta <u>London</u> Cairo Minsk Amsterdam Bangkok
      Not Amsterdam, continue:
      Jakarta London <u>Cairo</u> Minsk Amsterdam Bangkok
      Not Amsterdam, continue:
      Jakarta London Cairo <u>Minsk</u> Amsterdam Bangkok
      Not Amsterdam, continue:
      Jakarta London Cairo Minsk <u>Amsterdam</u> Bangkok
      Amsterdam found.
      [4 marks available — 1 mark for starting by comparing Jakarta, 1 mark for moving to next entry, 1 mark for continuing to compare with subsequent entries, 1 mark for stopping once Amsterdam is found]

   b) Jakarta <u>London</u> Cairo Minsk Amsterdam Bangkok
      Jakarta London <u>Cairo</u> Minsk Amsterdam Bangkok
      Cairo Jakarta London <u>Minsk</u> Amsterdam Bangkok
      Cairo Jakarta London Minsk <u>Amsterdam</u> Bangkok
      Amsterdam Cairo Jakarta London Minsk <u>Bangkok</u>
      Amsterdam Bangkok Cairo Jakarta London Minsk
      [4 marks available — lose 1 mark for each incorrect stage (entries yet to be sorted are shown in grey, entry being compared is underlined)]
      When doing an insertion sort, you can ignore all the entries that you haven't sorted yet, but you should make sure to keep writing them in at every stage.

   c) Asking for user input with an appropriate message. *[1 mark]*
      Conditional statement to check input is of integer type. *[1 mark]*
      Conditional statement to check input is in correct range (0-6). *[1 mark]*
      Outputting suitable responses for invalid inputs. *[1 mark]*
      Accessing the correct item from the array. *[1 mark]*
      Outputting a suitable response using the array. *[1 mark]*
      E.g.
      number = input("Enter a number between 0 and 6.")
      if number is not an integer then
         print("Invalid Input Type")
      elseif number < 0 OR number > 6 then
         print("Invalid Number")
      else
         print("You have chosen " + conts[number])
      endif

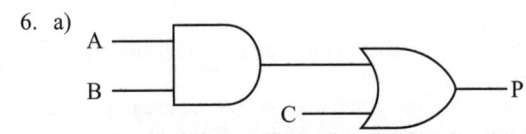

6. a) [Logic circuit diagram: A and B feed into an AND gate; the AND gate output and C feed into an OR gate; output is P]

   [3 marks available — 1 mark for A and B as inputs of an AND gate, 1 mark for the output of the AND gate and C as inputs of an OR gate, and 1 mark for P as the output of the OR gate]

   b)

A	B	C	P
FALSE	FALSE	FALSE	FALSE
FALSE	FALSE	TRUE	TRUE
FALSE	TRUE	FALSE	FALSE
FALSE	TRUE	TRUE	TRUE
TRUE	FALSE	FALSE	FALSE
TRUE	FALSE	TRUE	TRUE
TRUE	TRUE	FALSE	TRUE
TRUE	TRUE	TRUE	TRUE

   [3 marks available — 1 mark for every two correct rows]
   It doesn't matter what order you put the rows in, as long as every combination of true/false is covered.

7. a) Count-Controlled *[1 mark]*

   b) It sets a new variable, 'nextQuestion' *[1 mark]* equal to the next line of 'r1_Q.txt' (the next question and answers). *[1 mark]* It then separates the text into different variables ('question', 'answer1', 'answer2', 'answer3' and 'correctAnsNum') so they can be accessed individually by the program. *[1 mark]*

   c) E.g.
   ```
   01  quizfile = open("r1_Q.txt")
   02  quizScore = 0
   03  for n = 1 to 20
   04      nextQuestion = quizfile.readLine()
   05      split nextQuestion into the variables
            question, answer1, answer2, answer3, correctAnsNum
   06      print(question, answer1, answer2, answer3)
   07      userAnswer = input("Enter 1, 2 or 3:")
   08      if userAnswer == correctAnsNum then
   09          print("Correct!")
   10          quizScore = quizScore + 1
   11      else
   12          print("Wrong - bad luck!")
   13      endif
   14  next n
   15  print("Your score is ", quizScore, " out of 20")
   16  quizfile.close()
   ```
   [5 marks available — 1 mark for each correct line]
   Equivalent pseudocode expressions would also be accepted.

   d) Iteration for different columns (0 to 9). *[1 mark]*
   Iteration within this for different rows (0 to 5). *[1 mark]*
   Accessing Scores[x,y]. *[1 mark]*
   Adding up values for different columns. *[1 mark]*
   Calculating average. *[1 mark]*
   Outputting average. *[1 mark]*
   E.g.
   ```
   for y = 0 to 9
       total = 0
       average = 0
       for x = 0 to 5
           total = total + Scores[x,y]
       next x
       average = total / 6
       print("Round ", y, " average score is:", average)
   next y
   ```

   e) E.g.
   ```
   function diceEven(x, y)
       total = x + y
       if total MOD 2 == 0 then
           outcome = "Even"
       else
           outcome = "Odd"
       endif
       return outcome
   endfunction
   ```
   [5 marks available — 1 mark for each correct line]
   Your answer must be given in OCR Exam Reference Language or a high-level programming language or award no marks.

   f)

Test Data	Test Type	Accepted?
23	Normal	Yes
18	Boundary	Yes
15	Invalid	No
"Twelve"	Erroneous	No

   [4 marks available — 1 mark for each correct row]
   Any suitable erroneous test data will get the mark for the last row.

   g) Correct use of procedure. *[1 mark]*
   Asking for user input of name and age. *[1 mark]*
   Using a selection statement to check age. *[1 mark]*
   Outputting a suitable message if age is less than 18. *[1 mark]*
   Extracting the first three letters of a user's name and changing the string to uppercase. *[1 mark]*
   Concatenating user's name with age. *[1 mark]*
   E.g.
   ```
   procedure username()
       name = input("Enter your name:")
       age = input("Enter your age:")
       if age >= 18 then
           username = name.left(3).upper + str(age)
       else
           print("You are too young to play!")
       endif
   endprocedure
   ```
   Your answer must be given in OCR Exam Reference Language or a high-level programming language or award no marks.

Set B — Paper 1

1. a) E.g. Von Neumann architecture has data and instructions stored together in memory. *[1 mark]*

    b) E.g. A memory address is copied from the program counter to the MAR. *[1 mark]* The data/instruction at that address is copied to the MDR. *[1 mark]* The program counter is increased by 1 to point to the next instruction. *[1 mark]* The control unit decodes the instruction *[1 mark]* and the instruction is executed. *[1 mark]* The cycle restarts using the new instruction address in the program counter. *[1 mark]*
    [4 marks available in total]

    c) Any **two** differences, e.g.
    - RAM is volatile and ROM is non-volatile, *[1 mark]* meaning that data stored in RAM is lost when the power is turned off, while ROM retains its data. *[1 mark]*
    - RAM has a much greater memory capacity than ROM *[1 mark]* as RAM needs to hold the OS and all the applications being run, whereas ROM only holds data for some basic functions like startup. *[1 mark]*
    - RAM can be read from and written to *[1 mark]* while ROM is read-only. *[1 mark]*
    - RAM stores data that is currently in use *[1 mark]* whereas ROM stores the boot up instructions for the system. *[1 mark]*
    [4 marks available in total]

    d) The ALU performs logical operations and calculations *[1 mark]* and the accumulator stores the intermediate results of these operations. *[1 mark]*

    e) E.g.
    - Not all software supports multicore processing. *[1 mark]*
    - Certain tasks cannot be split evenly between cores. *[1 mark]*
    - Other factors affect a system's performance, such as:
        - clock speed *[1 mark]*
        - cache size/type *[1 mark]*
        - amount of RAM *[1 mark]*
        - amount of secondary storage *[1 mark]*
        - the specifications of the dedicated GPU *[1 mark]*
    [3 marks available in total]

2. a) Any **two** characteristics, e.g.
    - price *[1 mark]*
    - reliability *[1 mark]*
    - read/write speed *[1 mark]*
    - durability *[1 mark]*
    - capacity *[1 mark]*
    [2 marks available in total]
    Wondering what the difference between reliability and durability is? Reliability is about how likely a product is to fail over time under general use, durability is more about how 'tough' the product is, e.g. to withstand knocks or cope with excessive usage.

    b) E.g.
    - The university would not be able to access files kept in cloud storage if they lost their Internet connection, *[1 mark]* while magnetic tape would always be accessible. *[1 mark]*
    - If Gail wants quick access to individual files, cloud storage would be faster than magnetic tape *[1 mark]* because tape uses sequential access, making it slow to find specific files. *[1 mark]*
    - A cloud storage system would likely charge a subscription, *[1 mark]* which would be more expensive, especially in the long term, than magnetic tape which is very cheap per GB. *[1 mark]*
    - Data kept in cloud storage is vulnerable to hacking, *[1 mark]* while this is not a problem for magnetic tape. *[1 mark]*
    - If there was a disaster such as a fire at the university, data stored on magnetic tape could be destroyed, *[1 mark]* while data stored in the cloud would be safe. *[1 mark]*
    [6 marks available in total — benefits and drawbacks of both options must be discussed for full marks]

    c) E.g.
    CDs would not be suitable as they can only hold around 700 MB of data. *[1 mark]*
    USB pen drives would be suitable, as they are cheap/portable/fast and store a suitable amount of data. *[1 mark]*
    External HDDs would not be suitable as obtaining 30 of them would be very expensive/excessive to store only 5 GB of data on each one. *[1 mark]*

3. a) A network interface controller allows a device to connect to a network. *[1 mark]*

    b)
Switch	Router	Wireless Access Point
	✓	

    [1 mark]

    c) Any **one** advantage, e.g.
    - Wired networks are generally faster than wireless networks, *[1 mark]* as they have a greater bandwidth/can transfer more data per second. *[1 mark]*
    - Wired networks are more reliable than wireless networks *[1 mark]* because the signal quality is not affected by factors like interference/distance from the switch/WAP. *[1 mark]*

    Any **one** disadvantage, e.g.
    - Wired networks are less flexible/convenient than wireless networks. *[1 mark]* For example, employees would no longer be able to easily connect devices such as phones and tablets/be able to move between offices while staying connected to the network with a wireless device. *[1 mark]*
    - It would be expensive to change over to a wired network *[1 mark]*, as they would have to purchase new hardware, e.g. a wired switch and large amounts of Ethernet cable/ it would take a long time for specialist IT staff to install the new cabling in all the offices. *[1 mark]*
    [4 marks available in total]

    d) Any **two** possible advantages, e.g.
    - Peer-to-peer networks have no centralised management *[1 mark]* whereas a client-server network would have a central server to deploy and manage security, backups, software, etc. *[1 mark]*
    - Peer-to-peer networks often create copies of files between devices, whereas client-server keeps a single, up-to-date file on the central server, *[1 mark]* which makes it easier to keep track of files as they are edited. *[1 mark]*
    - On peer-to-peer networks, machines may slow down when other machines access them, *[1 mark]* while servers are designed to handle lots of traffic without slowing down. *[1 mark]*
    - In a peer-to-peer network, when a user turns off their machine, the other network users lose access to any files on that machine, *[1 mark]* whereas servers are dedicated machines that are usually left on all the time. *[1 mark]*
    [4 marks available in total]

    e) DNS servers translate a website's domain name into an IP address *[1 mark]* so that a web browser can access the web page/resource. *[1 mark]*

4. a)
Data	Order of size
3 MB	3
6 nibbles	4
1.6 PB	1
500 TB	2
2 bytes	5

    [3 marks available — award 3 marks for all rows correct, award 2 marks for only 3 rows correct, award 1 mark for 1-2 rows correct]

b) i) 01000001 *[1 mark]*
   65 = 64 + 1, so 1s go in the corresponding bit positions.

   ii) 6 in hexadecimal = 0110 in binary
   — these become the first four digits.
   5 in hexadecimal = 0101 in binary
   — these become the second four digits. *[1 mark]*
   So, put these together to get:
   65 in hexadecimal = 01100101 in binary. *[1 mark]*

c) 1 0 0 1 1 1 1 1 +
   0 0 1 1 1 1 0 1
   ‾‾‾‾‾‾‾‾‾‾‾‾‾‾‾‾
   1 1 0 1 1 1 0 0
   ₁ ₁ ₁ ₁ ₁ ₁
   [2 marks available — 1 mark for each correct nibble]

d) An overflow error occurs when a computer system attempts to process a number that has too many bits for it to handle/attempts to store more than 8 bits as a byte. *[1 mark]*

e) E.g. Unicode® *[1 mark]* — uses multiple bytes for each character/covers all major languages. *[1 mark]*

5. a) Phishing *[1 mark]*

   b) E.g.
   - Anti-virus software could scan all incoming emails and attachments *[1 mark]*, and automatically quarantine/delete any potential threats before they reach the user's inbox. *[1 mark]*
   - A firewall could block emails from unknown/suspicious senders. *[1 mark]*
   - Anti-virus software can provide an 'are you sure' warning before allowing the user to open any attachments from unknown senders. *[1 mark]*
   [2 marks available in total]

   c)

A piece of malware was...	Virus	Worm	Trojan
...found in an email attachment sent by an unfamiliar charity.	✓		
...disguised as a popular open-source application.			✓
...self-replicating without interaction from Nick.		✓	

   [1 mark for each correct tick]

6. a) E.g. Using the maximum resolution will mean the file size of each photo will be large *[1 mark]*. He is unlikely to be able to store many of these images on the camera's storage *[1 mark]*.

   b) Any **two** pieces of metadata, e.g.
   - GPS data/where the photo was taken *[1 mark]*
   - Timestamp/when the photo was taken *[1 mark]*
   - What camera was used to take the photo *[1 mark]*
   - The photograph's file format *[1 mark]*
   - The image's dimensions/height/width/resolution *[1 mark]*
   - The image's colour depth/colour model *[1 mark]*
   [2 marks available in total]

   c) The computer takes the analogue sound wave picked up by the microphone *[1 mark]* and takes regular samples of the height of the wave to convert it into a digital/binary format which can be stored in an audio file. *[1 mark]*

d) Any **two** differences, e.g.
   - Lossy compression greatly reduces the file size *[1 mark]* while the reduction with lossless compression is only small. *[1 mark]*
   - Lossy compression can reduce the quality of the file *[1 mark]* while lossless files maintain the quality of the original. *[1 mark]*
   - Lossless files can be decompressed back into the original file, *[1 mark]* whereas the original cannot be retrieved from a lossy file. *[1 mark]*
   [4 marks available in total]

7. a) Any **two** security measures, e.g.
   - Data encryption *[1 mark]*
   - User account control/access levels *[1 mark]*
   - Password protection *[1 mark]*
   - Pattern/PIN/fingerprint scanner/retina scanner *[1 mark]*
   - Firewalls *[1 mark]*
   - Automatic security updates *[1 mark]*
   [2 marks available in total]

   b) Drivers act as 'translators' between the OS and the hardware, *[1 mark]* so Joel needs the driver in order for the printer to understand the data it is being sent and be able to print it correctly. *[1 mark]*

   c) i) Disk defragmentation utility *[1 mark]*

      ii) E.g. The utility would collect together any parts of files that have been separated (fragmented) *[1 mark]* and reorganise them in an efficient way on the disk. *[1 mark]* This means that the read/write head in the HDD can access files with less movement, increasing the drive's performance. *[1 mark]*
      [3 marks available in total]

8. Points you might include:

   Impact on software developers
   - Pirated software will lead to reduced income for software developers, which in turn could affect their standard of living.
   - Software developers could lose their jobs as companies go out of business, damaging the software development industry as a whole.
   - Software developers might be forced to add extra measures to their software to prevent/discourage piracy (e.g. digital rights management), which can make the software less convenient for people who are trying to use it legitimately.

   Legal issues
   - The person illegally downloading the software is breaking the law, risking criminal prosecution for a piece of software.
   - Websites hosting the files/providing links to the files are at risk of prosecution (although sites that allow people to upload their own files are a legal grey area).
   - The software developers could pursue a legal case against the person downloading the software illegally or the website hosting the links to the software, under the Copyright, Designs and Patents Act 1988.
   - Because of the international nature of the Internet and varying worldwide copyright laws, it can be difficult to take legal action against people who pirate software.
   - If strict copyright laws are introduced to prevent piracy, this could begin to affect jobs that rely on being able to use sections of copyrighted materials, such as journalism.

Ethical issues
- Software is often expensive to buy legally which many people cannot afford to do, so piracy could be seen as reducing the digital divide.
- The more software that is downloaded illegally, the more money people are effectively stealing from software companies, limiting their ability to produce more software/maintain current software/employ staff.
- Governments may be pressured into devoting time/staff/budget resources into blocking websites that are distributing software illegally, at the expense of other areas such as healthcare.
- If no action is taken against illegal downloads, this could endorse the attitude that it isn't a problem and encourage more people to commit the same crime.

Cultural implications
- If a country has relaxed copyright laws, it could be taken advantage of by people in countries with strict copyright laws. This might lead to pressure between governments to change their copyright legislation.
- If the software company decided to pursue legal action, this could lead to bad press, putting the company in a negative light.
- Companies who do not pursue legal action could be seen as a target for criminals for future illegal downloads.
- Society in general could overlook the legal aspects of this activity and almost ignore the fact that they are committing a crime.
- If paid-for software becomes easy to obtain for free, then open source software might become less popular, which could damage the online communities that support these types of projects.

How to mark your answer:
- Two or three brief points with very little explanation. *[1-2 marks]*
- Three to five detailed points covering at least two of: impact on software developers, legal issues, ethical issues and cultural implications. *[3-5 marks]*
- Six or more detailed points that form a well-written, balanced discussion, covering all of: impact on software developers, legal issues, ethical issues and cultural implications. *[6-8 marks]*

Set B — Paper 2

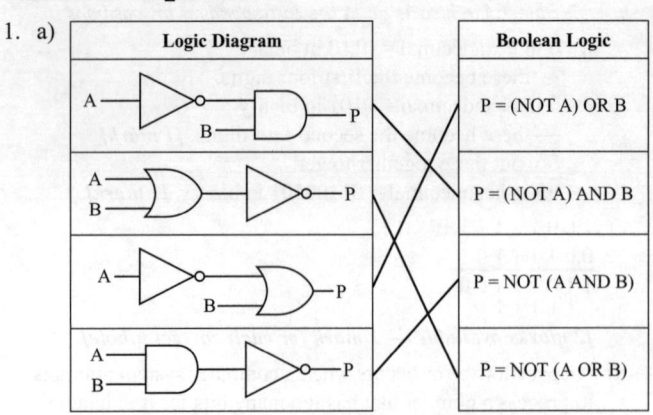

1. a) [Logic Diagram to Boolean Logic matching question]

   [2 marks available — award 2 marks for all connections correct, award 1 mark for at least two connections correct]

   b)
A	B	P
0	0	0
0	1	1
1	0	0
1	1	0

   [2 marks available — 1 mark for every two correct rows]
   You could also use TRUE for 1 and FALSE for 0.

   c) Accepting user inputs of library card and passcode. *[1 mark]*
   Assigning Boolean value to librarycardValid. *[1 mark]*
   Assigning Boolean value to passcodeValid based on user input. *[1 mark]*
   Correct use of librarycardValid and passcodeValid in determining the value of openDoor. *[1 mark]*
   Correctly testing time of day in determining the value of openDoor. *[1 mark]*
   E.g.
   input library card
   libarycardValid = check library card is registered on system
   passcode = input("Please enter the passcode.")
   passcodeValid = check passcode is correct
   if librarycardValid AND passcodeValid AND time >= 7 AND time <= 18 then
       openDoor = true
   endif

2. SELECT Destination *[1 mark]*
   FROM holiday *[1 mark]*
   WHERE Cost <= 400 *[1 mark]*

3. a) *E.g.*
   filenameValid = false
   do
       filename = input("Enter a filename.")
       if filename.length > 30 then
           print("Filename too long.")
       else
           filenameValid = true
       endif
   until filenameValid == true
   save file to server as filename
   print(filename + " has been successfully saved to the server.")
   [4 marks available — 1 mark for each correct line]
   Equivalent pseudocode expressions would also be accepted.

   b) Any **one** validation check, e.g.
   - Check the filename doesn't contain any symbols, such as @ or ! *[1 mark]*
   - Check the filename has actually been entered. *[1 mark]*
   - Check the filename has an appropriate file extension, such as .txt. *[1 mark]*
   [1 mark available in total]

c) i) Defensive design is the practice of making a program more robust and anticipating/preventing misuse by users. *[1 mark]*

   ii) E.g. It can make the program less user-friendly / affect the functionality of the program. *[1 mark]*

4. a)

Record	Array	String
	✓	

[1 mark]

b)
1. Grape | Pear | Tomato | Fig | Mango | Kale | Apple | Cherry
2. Grape | Pear | Tomato | Fig   Mango | Kale | Apple | Cherry
3. Grape | Pear | Tomato | Fig   Mango | Kale   Apple | Cherry
4. Grape | Pear   Tomato | Fig   Mango | Kale   Apple | Cherry
5. Grape | Pear   Fig | Tomato   Kale | Mango   Apple | Cherry
6. Fig | Grape | Pear | Tomato   Apple | Cherry | Kale | Mango
7. Apple | Cherry | Fig | Grape | Kale | Mango | Pear | Tomato

[4 marks available — 1 mark for splitting initial list into halves until each list is one item long, 1 mark for merging and sorting single items into two-item lists, 1 mark for repeating until list is merged, 1 mark for final sorted list]

c) Apple | Cherry | Fig | Grape | Kale | Mango | Pear | Tomato
n = 8, so (n + 1)/2 = 9/2 = 4.5, which rounds to 5:
Apple | Cherry | Fig | Grape | **Kale** | Mango | Pear | Tomato
"Kale" is alphabetically <u>after</u> "Cherry", so delete the second half of the list:
Apple | Cherry | Fig | Grape
Now n = 4, so (n + 1)/2 = 5/2 = 2.5, which rounds to 3:
Apple | Cherry | **Fig** | Grape
"Fig" is alphabetically <u>after</u> "Cherry", so delete the second half of the list:
Apple | Cherry
Now n = 2, so (n + 1)/2 = 3/2 = 1.5, which rounds to 2:
Apple | **Cherry**
"Cherry" has been found.
[4 marks available — 1 mark for comparing "Cherry" to "Kale", 1 mark for deleting the second half of the list, 1 mark for a further comparison, 1 mark for correctly finding "Cherry"]

d) E.g. Linear search *[1 mark]*

5. a) Error diagnostics will display the location of an error and may suggest possible fixes. *[1 mark]*
A run-time environment will allow Julian to execute and test his code within the IDE as he writes it. *[1 mark]*

b) Iterative testing is carried out throughout the development of a program, *[1 mark]* whereas final testing is carried out at the end of development to check the final program is working as intended. *[1 mark]*

c) Logic error: the program will follow BODMAS and do the division before the subtraction, which is not what is intended. *[1 mark]*
Syntax error: the comparison operator '==' has been used instead of the assignment operator '='. *[1 mark]*

d) Opening a file called 'Daily_Temps.txt'. *[1 mark]*
Accepting input of temperature (in F) on a loop. *[1 mark]*
Correctly calling convertFC function. *[1 mark]*
Correctly writing data to the file. *[1 mark]*
Ending the loop with an appropriate condition. *[1 mark]*
Closing the file. *[1 mark]*
E.g.
file = open("Daily_Temps.txt")
do
    F = input("Enter temperature in F")
    C = convertFC(F)
    file.writeLine(C, " Celsius")
    continue = input("Continue? (Y/N)")
until continue == "N"
file.close()
Remember — if a question doesn't specify how to give your answer, you can give your answer as pseudocode or a flowchart. Using OCR Exam Reference Language or a high-level programming language is fine too.

6. a) Any **two** benefits, e.g.
- Coding is easier as code is only written to carry out simple tasks. *[1 mark]*
- It is easier to test the program as each module can be tested individually. *[1 mark]*
- Individual sub programs and modules can be fixed without affecting the rest of the program. *[1 mark]*
- Modules can be reused in other programs in the future. *[1 mark]*

[2 marks available in total]

b)

Feature	Line(s)
Boolean data	03, 08
Iteration	02, 06 (or 02-06)
String data	07, 10

[3 marks available — 1 mark for each row]

c) The variable soilMoisture will be increased by less each loop, so it will take more loops to reach 50. *[1 mark]* Since the amount of water that the plants receive in each loop has not changed, this means that the plants will receive more water overall. *[1 mark]*

d) Any **two** ways, e.g.
- Use indentation (i.e. in the IF statement and DO UNTIL loop) *[1 mark]*
- Include more comments *[1 mark]*
- Use sub programs *[1 mark]*
- Use constants (i.e. 1.5 in line 05 could be a constant) *[1 mark]*

[2 marks available in total]

7. a) i) E.g. *title.subString(i, 1)* is a string *[1 mark]*, so *y* must be a string so they can be concatenated *[1 mark]*.

ii)

x	i	y
7	–	"2020"
–	0	"2020F"
–	2	"2020Fr"
–	4	"2020Fre"
–	6	"2020Fre!"

[4 marks available — 1 mark for each correct row]

b)

	Normal	Invalid	Boundary	Erroneous
"Moon Centaurs"	✓			
"Outpost"			✓	
"Luna"		✓		

[1 mark for each correct tick]

c) Generating a random integer between 0 and 4. *[1 mark]*
Retrieving the correct element from the array. *[1 mark]*
Printing a suitable message to the user. *[1 mark]*
E.g.
array genres = ["Fantasy", "Crime", "Romance", "Sci-Fi", "Western"]
choice = random(0, 4)
chosenGenre = genres[choice]
print("Why not try " + chosenGenre + " today?")
Your answer must be given in OCR Exam Reference Language or a high-level programming language or award no marks.

d) E.g.
fileName = input("Enter an audiobook filename.")
audioSize = fileSize(fileName)
if audioSize >= 1.5 then
    print("Error — file too large.")
endif
[4 marks available — 1 mark for each correct line]
Your answer must be given in OCR Exam Reference Language or a high-level programming language or award no marks.

e)

Sequence	Selection	Iteration
		✓

[1 mark]

f) 03: Sets total to 0 at the start of the loop for each staff member. *[1 mark]*
06: Adds the input sales value to the running total. *[1 mark]*
07: Keeps looping sales input until 0 is input. *[1 mark]*
08: Calculates the bonus as 0.1 times their total sales. *[1 mark]*

g) Jesse gets a £20 bonus.
Anabelle gets a £16 bonus.
Roland gets a £3 bonus.
[3 marks available — 1 mark for correct format of each line, 1 mark for 1 correct value of 'bonus', 1 mark for all correct values of bonus]

h) Checking sales is non-negative using an appropriate statement. *[1 mark]*
Appropriate output message for a negative sales value. *[1 mark]*
Checking the value of bonus. *[1 mark]*
Correct adjustment of bonus if total is greater than 500. *[1 mark]*
Correct adjustment of bonus if total is less than or equal to 100. *[1 mark]*
Correct output of bonus with condition-controlled loop to continue (as in the original program). *[1 mark]*
Your answer must be given in OCR Exam Reference Language or a high-level programming language or award no marks.
E.g.
do
    name = input("Enter staff name")
    total = 0
    do
        sales = input("Enter value of item sold (£)")
        if sales >= 0 then
            total = total + sales
        else
            print("Negative sales value entered.")
        endif
    until sales == 0
    if total > 500 then
        bonus = total * 0.15
    elseif total <= 100 then
        bonus = total * 0.05
    else
        bonus = total * 0.1
    endif
    print(name + " gets a £" + str(bonus) + " bonus.")
    continue = input("Continue? (Y/N)")
until continue == "N"

CGP

www.cgpbooks.co.uk

COP42U